Organize for Cancer

How to Get Through Treatment And Recover Easier

Organize for Cancer

How to Get Through Treatment and Recover Easier

Cynthia Braun

Parker House Publishing

To Mom and Dad,
For teaching me to never give up
And that anything worth having in life
Is worth fighting for

Acknowledgments

I thank all of my family and friends who guided me. I am so blessed to have you all in my life!

All of my appreciation and gratitude go to:

My husband, Allan, and my mom and dad who supported me from day one! Their compassion and strength made all the difference.

My BFF, Pam, who is not only an extremely caring nurse but also, my life-long friend.

My other wonderful friend, Randee, who helped me edit my manuscript's first draft, and also knows me for a very long time.

Andrea, my business coach, who believed my story should be told.

I would also like to thank Fran Drescher's book "Cancer Schmancer," which gave me hope while going through my cancer treatment with some laughs.

My surgeon, who saved my life with the first cancer diagnosis and continues to fight on behalf of women everywhere.

My oncologist at Memorial Sloan Kettering Cancer Center, who saved my life the second time I was diagnosed. She got me into the system quickly and approached my cancer with such positivity. I love her for that.

All of the doctors and nurses who have helped me, and are committed to helping others every day at Memorial Sloan Kettering Cancer Center.

My family

What people are saying...

Bravo to you Cynthia - you are an inspiration for those who unfortunately may walk in your shoes. Cancer touched your body but you kicked its butt.

Fran Greene LCSW, Relationship Coach

Cynthia built her team of loving family and friends with a non-stop selection of events, hobbies, and laughter to keep her proverbial sunny side up, up, up. Please - read this book; you'll find many ways to make her suggestions fit your life and combine them with your desire to come out strong, healthy, and loved.

Andrea Feinberg, MBA, Marketing That Rocks

I have known Cynthia for more than thirty years. She has always impressed me with her ability to face challenges and adversities with fortitude and a very positive growth mindset. Her inspirational book reveals how she has used her very positive personality and organizational skills to manage her treatment and recovery from cancer. She discusses how she was ready to take risks and use effective strategies to work her way through obstacles and back to good health!

Cindy Hittner, Speech Pathologist

When Cynthia told me what she'd just gone through - for the 2nd time - and how she managed it, I asked if I could read the book even in its rough form. Her very positive attitude and focus on loving support from the people in her life helped her tremendously. I went through my difficult recovery program having breast cancer; I commend you and support you on your journey.

Pamela Diamond License Practical Nurse

I knew my good friend had the strength and attitude to come through this awful ordeal. I was so glad I could be part of the process with her and, in reading her book, you'll be glad, too!

Maureen K. Calamia, Luminous Spaces

When Cynthia told me about her cancer diagnosis, I knew she would collect her wits and use her organizational talent to enable the success of her cancer surgery, therapy, and recovery to the utmost. Cynthia's strategy of organized positivity about treatment, nutrition, and wellness and her focus on love and support from family and friends is truly inspirational. Her book is a step-by-step guide to keeping a positive attitude and can teach all of us what to do for ourselves or a loved one when affected by a cancer diagnosis. Cynthia's book is a very moving must-read for anyone affected by this disease and their loved ones.

Paula Bennett

You mapped out step by step what you would do to make this a survivor's story. Having finished reading your story I can appreciate all the knots of life that you untied and managed to make the ride as smooth as possible. So proud of you Cynthia in putting this book together to help people go thru struggles be it Cancer or any struggles that are taking over their life. May health be the road you travel and your book land in the hands of those that need inspiration and direction.

Elaine Robbins

Her story is loaded with how-to's and lessons learned that will inspire anyone who is facing the scary challenges of living with cancer. Cynthia is truly a master of understanding human fortitude.

Nancy Borg, Professional Organizer

This book will ease the way for anyone on this journey.

Betty Pilnik, Oceanside, New York

Cynthia is an amazing woman with incredible energy, and the most organized person I know. She faced the tremendous challenges that a diagnosis and treatment plan for cancer pose with courage and fortitude. Her positive attitude and strength are an inspiration for all!

Dr. Amy Steinberg

I laughed, I cried. And I can't wait for the movie. I knew my good friend had the strength and attitude to come through this awful ordeal. I was so glad I could be part of the process with her and, in reading her book, you'll be glad, too!

Randee Silberfeld, CEO Psychiatric Billing

When Cynthia's response to cancer was to through a 'Good Vibes' party, I knew my good friend had the strength and attitude to come through this awful ordeal. I was so glad I could be part of the process with her and, in reading her book, you'll be glad, too!

Linda Stopsky, RN

Table of Contents:

Prologue

Here I was, a happy-go-lucky young woman who never had a major health issue in my 57 years of life. I always went to my internist every year for a routine checkup. I always went to my gynecologist for my annual exam and mammogram and sonogram. All that changed the day I heard from my doctor that I had cancer. This was the biggest challenge I'd ever faced. After the initial shock and fear set in, I then began to look at how to tackle this problem.

As a professional organizer for 20 years, I have experience working for clients who have faced enormous family and personal health challenges, and whose lives (and homes) have fallen into disarray because of the chaos* in their life. This was not going to happen to me! For my physical, emotional and spiritual well-being I decided I would face cancer from an organizer's point of view, using the skills that I had honed over the years to help so many others. Organizing often has an impact far beyond a cleaned room. It has such an impact on a person's attitude, sense of self, and possibility.

This book is a chronicle of my journey as a professional organizer going through the process of treatment, and the specific steps I took towards getting better and getting my life back on track. It is so easy to get "stuck" and depressed about a cancer diagnosis, but there are positive strategies to avoid the usual pitfalls and come up on top! As you will read, my relationships with family and friends were and remain a big part of this 'plan' and the healing process. I hope my story and experience inspire you in whatever challenges you may face.

Also, I hope when you finish reading my book that you will find hope and that recovery is not as bad as you expected. When you know what to expect the unknown is not as scary.

Introduction

On July 29, 2019, I received a diagnosis that I had uterine cancer. After a hysterectomy and radiation, I received a clean bill of health, only to get a recurrence of uterine cancer 2 years later, which had spread to both lungs. So, then I had to receive chemotherapy for 18 weeks, but I'm happy to report that I'm now in full remission (with a 2-year maintenance plan).

Anyone who knows me knows that family is wonderful. We have always been close. My mom and dad had me young so we were only 21 years apart in age. They gave me a wonderful childhood growing up in Lake Ronkonkoma, New York, or "Lawn Guylan" as we say it. It was very underdeveloped when we moved there in 1968. We had a brand-new custom-built home with a big backyard to play in and eventually had a pool. I'll get

to the pool later in the book. My two younger brothers and I are very close and speak weekly even though we are all busy with our careers and families. We are always there for each other, which was key during my cancer ordeal. I have always been an organized person and I found that having such structure and focus was very empowering throughout my life, both personal and professional.

Personally, when I was growing up my room was always very neat and organized. My clothes always had a particular home whether it was in drawers or hanging in the closet. I used to visit my friend Cheryl next door who had the same house and room as me and I would straighten it up with her every time I visited her since I couldn't play with everything in disarray.

Her mother loved when I came since she knew her daughter's room would be so much better off once I did my thing! I also used to visit my cousin in New Jersey for family weekends. This was my dad's only sibling so they were our only cousins. My mom was an only child and both her parents died when she was 16. I would also clean and organize her big beautiful room since she also had the same issue as my friend Cheryl. Clothes and items all over the place.

When I went to college my dorm room was used for tours when high school students would come to see the college before deciding where to go.

In my last year in college, I was my sorority's house president. Most of the sorority sisters lived in a large Victorian home right on the main road to the SUNY Oneonta campus. I made sure that it was always in pristine condition. I made the pledges do chores around the house to keep the CHAOS away (Can't Have Anyone Over Syndrome). So, as you can see, I always was an organized person. I guess I was born that way. My mom always kept our home clean and neat and there were never papers laying around. My dad had a tool room in the basement and he labeled the Similac formula cans with all his hardware, For example: ¼" screws, ¼" nails, ¼" washers, ½" screws, ¼" inch nails, ¼" washers, etc.... My dad also always kept the garage tidy since my mom parked in the one-car garage the entire time we lived there.

I helped my friends and family move into their homes and apartments throughout the years. I was always willing to help them to make the transition easier for all. I remember helping my friend Betty, who had just separated from her husband, move into her Oceanside condo with her 2 young boys. One of them is my daughter's best friend and we got everything done in 1 day. I felt relieved knowing that they were all settled into their new place before I left for Disney World with my family the next day! Of course, I was already packed and ready to leave for our big week vacation in Orlando, Florida. It was a well-planned vacation, too. Disney World with all 4 kingdoms and then Cape Canaveral and Universal Studios on separate days.

I planned our vacation out for every day to get the most out of our time. And of course, I made a fabulous scrapbook to show everyone and documented all our fun times. I usually scrapbook all our family trips and events shortly after the event while it's fresh in my mind. I am lucky enough to have a scrapbook room in my basement to do this fun activity on a regular basis. I have 102 scrapbooks, which includes everything I have done since senior year in high school when I first started scrapbooking.

Having all my memories in a scrapbook gives me the confidence of having great memories remembered throughout my life. My family and friends always enjoy looking at them. I have them in chronological order so it's easy to find what we are looking for. Especially when it was time to get photos for my daughter's and son's Bat and Bar Mitzvah video montages. People also ask me if they need a picture. Remember, we went digital around 2004 when everyone started getting smartphones but before then you developed pictures from a camera.

Remember those days? I am very organized when it comes to my pictures, I have the digital ones organized by year on CDs in a labeled book. This makes it easy to find a picture in a flash. For instance, my sorority had a 100th anniversary and I pretty much supplied 80 percent of the photos on the video montage.

So, I grew up organized and have been ever since. Getting through my cancer was easier since I felt more in control with all my planning and documenting everything. I hope you will learn at least one thing you can do if you ever find yourself (hopefully never) in my situation.

Chapter 1 The Diagnosis

(The Problem)

On July 20, 2019, I was diagnosed with Uterine Cancer Stage 0. It was a day that changed my life forever! Regardless of the stage, regardless of how educated I was, just hearing the words "I have cancer" I was still programmed to be devasted and terrified. The shock of it was compounded as I was a highly health-conscious woman; with great nutritional habits, never smoked or did drugs, exercised daily, never ignored physical signs, practiced stress reduction, and maintained medical care. How did this happen?

My doctor had recommended a sonogram and biopsy because I had vaginal bleeding 6 years after menopause and then I got the news. Unbeknownst to me, I had no idea that this might be something bad.

Let me rewind. I was at my niece's Bat Mitzvah in Las Vegas in June 2018. I had started bleeding the day before the party but I didn't think much of it. I just thought that I was having a period and I was "young" again. I never had problems with my menstrual cycle and gratefully got pregnant on the first try both times my husband and I wanted children. Never had a miscarriage or missed a period (only when I was pregnant, of course) I ate very healthy and had a healthy, active lifestyle all my life; I was on the swim team in High School and College. I was also a Lifeguard for the Town of Brookhaven on Long Island, NY where I grew up and continued to live. I had recently become a certified water instructor and taught water aerobics at a nearby country club and in our at-home pool. I never smoked or did drugs. I belonged to a local health club/gym since I graduated college in 1983. Now I have a gym in my basement with many machines and free weights. I enjoy my ability to keep myself fit and healthy.

On our way home from Las Vegas my husband finds out that he is losing his job. So, what does any good wife do, but work even more than usual to give us more savings and more of a cushion and time before he can find another job. I completely ignored the menstrual signs and carried on with my daily life.

Yet, feeling the stress on me more than ever, I buried myself in my organizing work. I get a great feeling of satisfaction from helping others get rid of the clutter and organize their lives, room by room, in their homes or apartments. Being a professional organizer gave me a great skill set to overcome many obstacles. I never was a procrastinator so I did what I was expected to do and go for my annual OBGYN exam, which was due in July, shortly after our Las Vegas trip. The routine exam showed no signs of abnormality so I just continued with my life.

It wasn't until June 2019 - a year later - that I would have a "period" again, as I sort of thought at that time. It was time again to go for my annual exam and explain to the doctor my concerns. Why was I bleeding again? I asked myself. The doctor thought I just needed a D&C. A dilation and curettage procedure is a surgical procedure in, which the cervix is dilated so that the uterine lining (endometrium) can be scraped with a spoon-shaped instrument to remove abnormal tissues. However, I had a sonogram taken just to make sure. The sonogram revealed many fibroids in my uterus area so she ordered a biopsy on the tissue to be done the following week. My mom was with me and wasn't really concerned since my health was pretty good. The doctor said I would get the results of the biopsy in a week or two.

I'll never forget this moment: I was in New York City organizing with a client when I saw my phone caller ID come up for my gynecologist. So, I picked it up and the person on the other end said the doctor has the results of your biopsy and would like to explain it in person. I was quite a distance away and said that I wouldn't be able to get there until 7 pm. They said the doctor will stay open to see me.

I knew then something was wrong! It was very hard to drive to her since, all the way, my heart was palpitating and I couldn't believe something bad was happening to my body. My health had always been good and I took care of myself. So, when I entered the doctor's office the receptionist sent me in right away saying "the doctor is waiting for you." As my heart was beating a mile a minute, I blurted out "tell me what it is!" As she said, "Uterine CANCER," I nearly fainted on the table. She gave me a glass of water and then my mind was able to focus. I had to remind myself to focus as she spoke those ill-fated words. Then, once I digested the diagnosis, my mind naturally went into organizer mode!

My profession was my ally in nearly everything; I knew it would support me now:

- What is the next step?
- What do I need to do now?
- What could I have done to prevent this from happening?

She said, with confidence, that I am going to be fine and that all I needed was a hysterectomy. I asked if she could do it tomorrow. Hysterectomy meant the removal of my uterus, fallopian tubes, and ovaries. Laughing, she explained she doesn't do this type of surgery and that I would have to find a surgeon in my network. She could recommend names but didn't know if they took my insurance. Now, you remember: my husband lost his job a year prior and we were on the Affordable Care Act, which wasn't the best.

I was in tears. I couldn't talk. How would I tell my mom this news? The doctor would have to tell her directly so I quickly got out my cell phone and had my mother on speaker in seconds. The doctor was also my mom's OBGYN so that eased the quick conversation. Then, after I told her that I was at the doctor's office and she has something to tell her, the doctor proceeded to tell her my situation.

My mother was silent and *my mom is never lost for words.* Yet, she was speechless for a few seconds. "Ok," she said, "what do we need to do now?" Then the doctor repeated what she had told me. My mom said she would start to make calls as soon as she got off the phone but she would meet me at home to tell my husband, Allan, in fifteen minutes.

Now, my husband had developed diabetes from the stress of losing his job the year prior but was doing better now. I didn't want to jeopardize his health by worrying about me. Luckily, my mom lived nearby. I left the doctor's office, hopeful that everything was going to be OK. We both arrived at my home at 7:45 and shortly afterward, Allan returned home from the supermarket.

We told him to sit down so we could give him some news. He too was speechless and in shock by the cancer news. He actually said "Oh shit!" I guess that was his first reaction and then he broke down and cried. My mom assured him with what the doctor had said about this type of endometrial cancer.

I then told our daughter and called our son in California to tell him the news of my Uterine Cancer. My kids were upset and knew that I was strong and that I would get through this with flying colors. The more I said it, the more it felt real although I continued to feel I was kind of in a fog.

Then I called both my brothers to relay the news. We are a very close family and I wanted them to know right there and then. I needed their support and they both said that I would be fine. My body was basically healthy and the surgery will be a piece of cake! With that reminder, we had to find a surgeon, so we proceeded to our home office to get on the computer. We started looking for a surgeon to perform the hysterectomy, asap. Telling my immediate family was heart-wrenching but I got through it.

The next step was to put our heads together to formulate a plan. My mom took copies of my reports, and the names of doctors and called their offices to ask if they took my insurance. She would make the calls since I was scheduled to work with a client the next day; I had no plan to set business aside. My mom was great at doing this; she has had a lot of practice since both she and my dad have had many health issues and have seen a number of medical specialists.

So, this is the beginning of my journey with cancer.

It was unexpected, frightening, and complicated; however, I knew I had many resources to assist me. You too may be blessed with family, friends, or even a health-related background. Take advantage of whatever resources you have available to you!

Yet, while I was lucky to have all this, I also had a skill and professional training that I immediately realized would be an added 'secret weapon' in my cancer journey. Believe me: I don't make light of this awful disease that continues to kill so many and scar so many families. I knew I had a life-changing challenge ahead. And I was able, in that moment of initial shock, to realize my training would be my partner, just as my medical team and loved ones were.

As a professional organizer, I used my skills to help me go through the painful process. There are many benefits of being organized but first and foremost it gave me the control I needed and a perfect outline of how I would have a clear and concise path to take on the disease, head-on.

I will take you through each step and what I did at every turn. I journaled my entire cancer journey so I could remember everything I did, so, hopefully, you can learn from my mishaps and successes. I also had a sizable network of friends, a Feng Shui practice, and a religious community that I had built over the years that I could harness to support me in the fight to recover and do it well.

My family and friends were all in shock by the news, but I had to focus on myself – in order to survive this and thrive!!

I needed to let myself feel! I knew if I held back, it would probably induce anxiety, which did happen. As an organizer, I felt I can control my feelings, however in certain aspects you can. I wanted to keep my life structured every day. I keep busy socially but you may want to just take a mindful walk. I never had such bad anxiety. I felt horrible. I couldn't eat or sleep. It was the darkest time in my life. It took a while but I was able to find a therapist who is can talk to and receive medication. After many trials and errors, we found the right combination of medications to help relieve the anxiety which was Prozac and then Olanzapine for sleep which I still take now. I never want to feel that bad again. All I did was cry and I felt helpless until several months when the medicine was the right amount and combination.

So, this is what I did to cope. I knew as an organizer I realized that it was more than I can handle alone. I planned trips which I will go into detail over the next chapters and also scheduled fun activities that made me feel good like massages, pedicures, and manicures. I also listened to upbeat music. I am lucky that I live near a beach where there is a walking nature path which I did almost every day to relieve my stress. Sometimes alone and more times with friends. I felt better when I was with someone hence, I didn't feel alone and depressed as much. Granted I knew I was depressed. Who wouldn't be with a diagnosis of cancer! Will I live through it or will I die was always in my thoughts. Even if you don't have the means to go on a trip or get personal services just do something positive. "I said to myself the Serenity Prayer: "God grant me the Serenity to accept the things I cannot change, the Courage to change the things I can and the Wisdom to know the difference." Practice self-care. Try to get the right amount of sleep. I also did a lot of scrapbooking which is a huge hobby that I have enjoyed over the last 35 years.

I also recommend reaching out to support groups in your area which I did. I spoke to others who went through the same diagnosis as me with both my cancers and asked many questions to be more prepared for the worse. It really helped knowing I wasn't the only one that felt so dark and helpless. They gave me hope knowing that they beat cancer. With the help of my therapist, I was able to reduce my anxiety and lessen my depression. She taught me the tapping method to help me relax, and I definitely recommend talking to someone. I even talked to my friend who is a therapist and she said something poignant to me early on: that I am still Cynthia who loves her husband kids, family, friends, and her career as an organizer I just have cancer now! That put my mind more at ease. I continued to struggle emotionally throughout both diagnoses but I hope you will find my method of approach inspiring.

My Daily Mantra

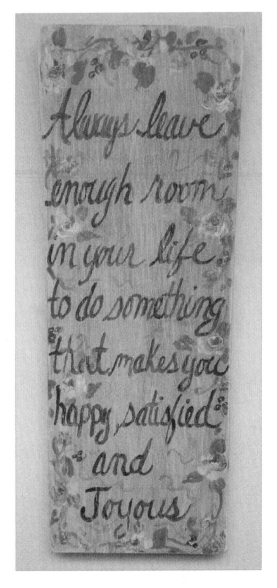

Chapter 2 The Doctors

(Introducing My Solution to Better Health)

My life, as my mom would express it, was "through rose-colored glasses." I had a wonderful childhood and a successful school and dating life. I have a loving family and many wonderful friends. I always thought positively. I was a happy person! Until cancer hit me like a brick wall. It came out of nowhere! Now I had to educate myself so I went online and researched my kind of cancer. Afterward, with some knowledge, I began to take the next steps:

My gynecologist, Dr. S. (she had been my gynecologist since before my daughter was born in 1993) was very optimistic since my illness was all contained in the uterus. My gynecologist's sister-in-law had the same diagnosis ten years prior and was perfectly fine now. At first, before she did the biopsy, Dr. S. thought I just needed a Dilation and Curettage (D & C). She even told this to my mom who drove me to the biopsy. I never had any procedures prior and the bleeding had stopped after three days. But then, two weeks later the biopsy confirmed it was uterine cancer! I never really heard of it so, of course, I did my due diligence and researched everything on it: the types of uterine cancer, the treatment recommendations, the stages and what they meant, recovery, and long-term effects. I researched on the internet and through word of mouth, I found a surgeon who specializes in this type of surgery, 45 miles away from my home.

After my consultation with the surgeon, Dr. B., she reassured me and my mom that I would be fine since my health was very good besides having-cancer. She told us she has performed 5-6 of these procedures daily over the 25 years of her medical career. So, I had a scheduled hysterectomy for September 19, 2019. Step 1 is done. Check off.

The next step in my plan was to meet with Dr. J., an integrative Healing Wellness Doctor (Step 2). I had a one-hour consultation and had many questions to ask her. She would do a full blood work on me and, once that was completed, she would do:

1. comprehensive evaluation & medical history

2. full detoxification to reduce inflammation and heal the gut
3. weekly nutrition consults
4. review physical activity and exercise
5. balance my hormones before and after detox

I would be prescribed vitamins and mineral supplements to gain proper nutritional balance. It was a six-month program and I could consult with her as often as needed. I felt that she and her staff would be a great support to help me before and after my surgery. Again, my meals would be well-planned and include my supplements.

After the meeting with Dr. J., I went to a local market and bought Italian Wedding Soup and a bouquet of flowers to take with me to visit my dear friend, Pam who was in the hospital. I hung out awhile to keep her company, shifting attention from myself to the needs of a dear friend, and then finally told her the news; this was such a relief for me. She totally understood everything since she had a hysterectomy five years before but under different circumstances. She also had endured breast cancer over ten years ago so it was prevalent. Then I discussed with her my plan for a party I would host to put me in a great mood, surrounded by so many loving friends. This would also keep me focused on something really positive, which I enjoy doing!

Before the party, I asked each of my girlfriends to write on decorative paper something to inspire me, which I read the morning of my surgery in the prep room. It gave me such a wonderful feeling in my heart while reading them aloud to my family who was there supporting me in the pre-surgical room.

I arranged another special event before surgery: my friend and colleague, Maureen, came to give me a Feng Shui consult. She also had been my instructor five years prior when I attended the Metropolitan Interior Design School where they had an accredited school for Feng Shui Certification. She gave me cures and blessings to rid the cancer and anxiety. She was amazing and my daughter and I implemented all the cures in my home. One cure was an orange and grapefruit peel bath. Then I went to the nursery to buy three indoor plants to be placed in certain areas to ground me. The Feng Shui training has had a strong, positive influence, both on me and my clients who use my organizing principles.

I also started to work with the nutritionist in the Integrative Wellness Program (www.Integrativehealingwellness.com.) I met the nutritionist at a healthy supermarket at 8 am one morning and learned what to eat and to avoid. I learned all about organic foods, plant-based foods, and the best foods for optimal health.

That's where things really changed for me. I became a clean eater, which means no salt, no sugar, and no oil. I had little to lose and a world of health to gain. I learned to make a healthy smoothie using fruits and vegetables and protein powder that would provide me energy in the morning. It was the substitute for breakfast. I reorganized the drawer that sits near the blender so this daily activity would be very easy to implement.

And it was.

Before surgery, I had some special times to celebrate. One was my husband's birthday and a bunch of us went to a beautiful, nearby beach. It was a beautiful day and it felt wonderful to relax. We brought our own lunch and stayed for dinner; there is a small café on the beach where you can buy hamburgers, lobster, fries, corn, and drinks. They also had a band, which was very entertaining. It was a perfect day!

Another celebration is a tradition in our family. All our wedding anniversaries are in August so we go out for a show and then dinner to celebrate. My mom and dad's anniversary is August 28, Michele and Matt's (my sister-in-law and my brother), is August 20, and my husband's and mine is August 13! Thus, we went to a show and then-enjoyed a delicious meal. Later in the week I met with my 2 besties from college and had lunch with them. I was telling them the story and all of a sudden, Alison started to cry. Little did I

know that six years prior she had a hysterectomy with the same surgeon. She never told anyone since it was more preventative with suspicious cells and so the doctor recommended that she remove everything related to the uterus, even her cervix. I knew that this was a clear sign; what were the chances that we would use the same surgeon? We lived in two different counties. I felt even more strongly that the surgery would go well since hers did too! They both were so supportive and since both lived near the hospital they promised to visit after surgery if I wanted company. They gave me such a warm feeling in my heart and I loved them even more!

On Wednesday, August 21 I started a new regime of a daily walk, 6:30 am - 8 am, at the beach with Elyse. I knew this would help me be calm and connect with nature. Elyse's husband had recently been diagnosed with rectal cancer and had surgery. She, being a nurse, was his nurse and supported him emotionally and physically every step of the way so he joined us on the daily walk, too. It was very therapeutic and calming. The weather was perfect - not too hot or too cold, yet perfect to walk so early near the water. It allowed us to get great physical activity before we all started our work day. It was a blessing for us to connect. She was so knowledgeable and also ate using the clean principles. She even grew her own organic vegetable garden in their backyard. Something I knew I would never do so I just bought organic fruits and vegetables at the farmer's market or in an organic market.

Later that day I had an hour and a half-interview with a Newsday (the Long Island newspaper) editor for the 60ᵗʰ-anniversary section on "Downsizing." I would appear as an organizing expert on how to let go of items when you are moving into a smaller dwelling. This was probably my 12ᵗʰ time appearing in Newsday, but who is counting...It was a great moment for me of validation for my professional life and choices.

In the mail came a bracelet from friends Amy and Alan with Hebrew and English words that read "Healing of the Body, Healing of the Soul." So sweet and caring of them. It touched my heart. I decided to wear the bracelet until my surgery.

Friday, August 23: I had to go for my CT scan with contrast. As I lay in the machine, I cried knowing what a mess I got into. I couldn't believe it was happening. I never had a CT scan since I never broke anything or was ever sick. Thankfully I was, once again, hosting a water yoga class with my friends in my backyard later that day; that got me out of my funk. I picked up food on the way home to serve an after-class lunch to everyone who attended. I felt the love and friendship of my friends that day. Hillary even bought me a "Good Vibes" Tee Shirt, which I planned to wear to my future party.

Before the surgery, I paid a visit to my colleague Sue who sold crystals and was a Crystal Feng Shui Coach. I knew her from my Feng Shui class and she became a full-time crystal coach. So, I bought Labradorite, a stone that is healing for my car, my desk, my night table, and in bracelet form to wear.

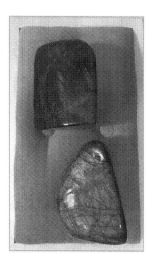

Even though my friend, Pam, was a great cook, I had to learn some cooking techniques to eat more cleanly. Before this, I never took an interest in cooking. My husband usually does all the cooking, especially on the grill, so I needed to learn some simple recipes. I couldn't rely on Pam or even Jody (You will read about her later) to cook for me. This was way out of my comfort zone but I had to learn so I did with the support of the Integrative Wellness staff.

Friday, August 30: I received a call from my surgeon's office about the result of the CT scan that had been taken the previous Friday. The great news is that the cancer was contained in my uterus; it didn't spread! I cried from happiness. I couldn't wait to tell everyone! I went text crazy and got so much positive feedback; I felt really good.

The next day a group of friends came out to spend the day, poolside. These were the last of the friends to hear the news. They were in shock, especially Jody who works for Dr. Thomas Campbell, the foremost authority on plant-based eating. Dr. Campbell wrote the book *China Study* published by BenBella Books (2006), which I read and now follow very strictly. With their visit, I had now personally told every one of my friends. Finally, I could move on to the next stage of my recovery plan.

I spent Sunday, September 1, with my mom in New York City to see the Marvelous Mrs. Maisel (Amazon Prime TV program) exhibit. We both loved the show so we thought it would be a hoot to see the exhibit and it was. Afterward, we did something else I always wanted to do: go to the Grand Bazaar on 8th Ave. in New York. It had many interesting items and I bought two stylish jackets. It was a beautiful day and my mom and I had a wonderful time together. I think she enjoyed it as much as I did since it was just the two of us.

Monday, September 2: After my morning walk at the beach, I went to get a massage. Janet, my massage therapist for the last 15 years, gave me a great massage and made me feel very relaxed so I decided to treat myself to more regular massages in my journey of wellness.

Later that day I held another water aerobics class, which was lots of fun, as usual. I have my steady people who come every  week and I enjoy the socialization while getting a great workout! Lesson learned: always get some physical activity every day to keep your positive hormone levels up.

My friend Alison, who had the surgery five years prior, told me to get a recliner since I would not be able to lay in my bed as my abdomen would be very sore from the surgery. I looked on Facebook Marketplace and found one that had been rarely used, not too far from our home. Allan and I went that evening to pick it up from the homeowner. It

31

was a blue velvety recliner that was in perfect shape. It still had the tags. The people were downsizing and needed to get rid of it. How convenient for me! Lesson learned: look to save money by buying things used instead of the full retail price.

 So, for the next couple of days, I organized with clients and then would have fun at night going to concerts or shows with Allan or my friends. Or I would take the day off and play Mah Jong in the pool. It was something to keep me busy and kept me in a positive mood. I took advantage of the great weather with great concerts and shows. I saw *Menopause, the Play* at a local community theatre. It was so relatable now. It gave us many laughs, which reminded me that I still had a lot of laughs to go in my life.

On Saturday, September 7, I went with Allan and the temple for a historical village tour, which was led by one of our members. It was fascinating and interesting about historical events that happened nearby. I then met up with my mom and Pam to attend a local craft fair. It's always a pleasure to go to this fair and find new and interesting things and creative people. The next day we went to the 'Welcome Back BBQ' at the temple that the Brotherhood men sponsor every year. It was great to see everyone and catch up with them. My mom and I then went to another craft fair, which was huge! It was another beautiful day and we found some goodies to buy. Lesson Learned: Spend time with friends, enjoy entertainment with small activities, and pamper yourself any way you can.

Monday. September 9: Went to my internist to get a medical exam for surgery clearance. My doctor was shocked to find out that I had cancer but reassured me that I would be fine and that recovery would be easy for me since I was already in very good shape. Later in the week, I went to a Women's Health Expo with my friend Ellice at the local Marriott Hotel. It was very informative and I learned a lot more about clean eating.

Chapter 3 Journal and Good Vibes Party

As stated in my journal (which I kept at my fingertips on my desk) Sunday, September 15th was a beautiful sunny day for my 'Good Vibes' party.

I decided to create this day to build and internalize a treasure of good feelings while going through this terrible, frightening time in my life. I had everyone write on special, decorative paper something to inspire me, which I would read the morning of my surgery in the prep room. It gave me such a wonderful feeling in my heart while reading them aloud to my family who was there supporting me in the pre-surgical room.

I had a cake specially made with the shape of my  pool (everyone knows I love my pool) and all the things around it. I had pink (my favorite color) balloons all over the backyard. I made a huge frame with the words GOOD VIBES for photo ops. I had it catered by a Greek restaurant that delivered and set up. I really lucked out since the weather was warm and sunny all day so it really was a pool party. Nearly all my friends made it. I also purchased online some beautiful, pink-flowered plates, cups, and bowls. The food was delicious and the highlight

was when I spoke about each person (or group of people) and how she had an impact on my life; as she came up on the deck, I gave her a hug and kiss. I had such gratitude for each and every one of them.

It took a while but everyone enjoyed learning how others had come into my life and all the fun memorable things we shared. And of course, I did it chronologically, starting with my mom and ending with the last wonderful friend I had made 2 years ago. I gave each one a favor (fancy nail Emory board). Who can't use one? I am probably the only person who doesn't use them. LOL! My friends all stayed longer than expected and I didn't mind at all.

I absolutely loved all the time spent with every one of them. The next time I would see my friends would be post-op.

Thursday, September 19: At 9 am the prep was started to clean out my bowels for surgery. I couldn't eat anything since they wanted my stomach empty. It was a tiresome day: taking Dulcolax, then MiraLAX then Pedialyte. It was challenging to say the least but it did the trick so I napped and eventually fell asleep until the next morning.

Chapter 4 Hysterectomy Surgery

(Second Step Toward Getting Better)

The surgery took place on September 20, 2019; it was the day after my mom's 79th birthday. All she wanted for her birthday that year was for me to get through the surgery successfully (and then get through four rounds of radiation). My family surrounded me in the pre-op room. I was very grateful to have them all there and I read all the cards everyone wrote at the Good Vibes party. As they wheeled me down the corridor to the operating room, I realized that I no longer would have menstrual issues. The 4-hour surgery went very well and Dr. B. said I should rest for a month and be a couch potato. Sounded great to me!

I stayed just one night and was already walking by the evening, attached to my IV. My husband, Allan, drove me home the next day and it felt more comfortable sitting in the recently purchased recliner chair than in bed. I slept in the chair for the entire 4 weeks. My sister-in-law came over with lasagna and chicken soup. That was so sweet of her. My mom came over, too, that first day. The first night I was in so much pain I woke up in the middle of the night, crying. The Motrin wasn't strong enough so Allan picked up prescribed Oxycodone at the pharmacy the next day. He's really good about getting me stuff. He is a wonderful, caring husband.

Visitors came and even sat with me in the backyard. We also had bought a gravity chair (a chair that evenly distributes weight along the length of the body and reduces pressure from the effects of gravity compared to traditional recliners) before surgery so I would be comfortable outside. Even though the pool was closed for the season, I couldn't go in it anyway since I had to keep the bandage dry. That fall happened to be beautiful weather; I guess it was the calm before the storm (COVID). Every day, someone (a family member or friend) came over since my husband had to go back to work a week later and I had three more weeks of recovery. We would talk about the day's events and the party that I just had.

Of course, I would scrapbook (I'm an avid scrapbooker) so I can show my friends the pictures from that amazing day. *Happy thoughts bring better healing days.*

I needed to learn to relax. For a person who is on the go (my life as a professional organizer calls for quite a lot of physical work and I teach swimming and water aerobics so I'm not at all accustomed to just sitting at home), it was quite an adjustment. I would watch TV, scrapbook, read books or–talk with my friends. My daughter, Rachel, worked from home so she was able to help me a lot with my meals. I was still very sore and had limited movement. I remember the surgeon specifically said to be a couch potato and absolutely no lifting or carrying. Something I had to learn to let go. You may also have to stop doing anything physical for four weeks.

Chapter 5 Healing Time

(Third Step Toward Getting Better)

I needed to learn how to relax. Something I rarely did. As I mentioned, I scrapbooked a lot, a hobby I have joyfully and successfully done for 40 years since I graduated high school. **See my organized scrapbook room below.**

I have 113 scrapbooks and, of course, they are all nicely organized on bookshelves. I used to go to scrapbook conventions with my mom (I got her into it) on the east coast throughout the years and, until 2015, there was a local scrapbooking store that gave classes. I continued journaling and did some painting during recovery but the best medicine was socializing. I loved when my friends visited me. It made the day go more quickly. I am not a big television watcher during the day. At night I like watching with my husband. So, every day a relative or a friend would come over and sit and talk with me. That was the best medicine for me.

Not working felt weird to me. I had never stopped working since I turned 16 (only when I went on vacation or gave birth to our two kids). Even when I worked my Fortune 100 job, I went for my MBA at night and, after I completed that, went to Interior Design School (Metropolitan School of Design) and worked at a furniture store on the weekends to get more experience. I thought I wanted to become an interior designer. My mom and I have been going to designer showcases every year since I was 15 years old. I loved and continue to go to them yearly.

I found that interior design didn't give me the quick satisfaction I was searching for; however, Professional Organizing and helping clients overcome obstacles gave me the satisfaction I was yearning for. So, after a month of healing, I was thrilled to be able to return to my organizing business. It helped me feel normal again and was a great distraction. Since it was a physical job, it helped me get back into my daily movement. I started slowly with my exercises. First, gentle yoga on the beach was my 'go-to', and then I graduated to walking on the beach again. When it got too cold, I then would walk on the treadmill I had in the basement.

I eventually also went back to my Integrative Wellness program eating organic and clean. I felt better and better as the gas and the pain subsided. After about a week, my friend Pam picked me up and we went to some bakeries to get a cake I needed for the Jewish holidays. The first night I had my family over but everyone pitched in and I didn't have to lift a finger. We were invited to a friend's home for the second night of Rosh Hashana dinner. I started to feel myself again and was grateful for it!

Chapter 6 Professional Organizing Career

(Finding My Niche)

Here's a little background on my business; you'll see why it was such a help with my recovery.

I discovered professional organizing after 9/11. I was at Dr. S's office, in the waiting room, and picked up one of the first issues of *Oprah Magazine*. I literally picked it up and was pleasantly surprised; there was an article about Julie Morgenstern, who was Oprah's professional organizer before Peter Walsh. I was so excited to read about this young, Jewish, divorced, woman raising two young children and doing tasks for people, and getting very nicely paid for her service.

I had a lightbulb moment as I was reading since I have been doing these kinds of tasks for friends and family since I was a young girl, not knowing it can be a profession! And of course, I enjoyed doing it. At the bottom of the article, there was a section saying if you are interested in becoming a Professional

Organizer write to NAPO, National Association of Professional Organizers, and, BOOM, did it hit me! So, of course, I wrote to them since there was no phone number or websites back in 2001. I received a letter 2 weeks later, thanking me for my interest and, if I wanted to find out more, there was a New York City chapter that met once a month. So, of course, I called the president of the NYC chapter and found out all the details and she invited me as a guest to the next meeting. I was thrilled to hear the guest speaker, Harold Taylor, a time management guru. I knew mostly what he was presenting, since working at a Fortune 100 company you get trained on everything: marketing, product, distribution, and time management.

Afterward, I stayed and talked to the NYC organizers. In fact, they approached me, since I was a new face among the 50 women who were present. They were delighted to see someone from Long Island. They all said they would be happy to refer me to their clients who move to the local suburbs. As New York City residents, they had no cars and really didn't want to leave the city; they were pretty much established with NYC clients. I was so appreciative.

The next week I went with my friend Gigi to get my DBA (Doing Business As) and business certificate. I decided on *Organize Your Life* since it seemed to create positive thoughts and a can-do attitude to get organized. That was my feeling at the time. So, excited with my new official papers, I went to Staples (an office supply store) and got some business cards made up. Remember - no websites for small businesses yet. So, I did many speaking engagements to get the word out and let the public know this service exists.

I would organize on my days off and weekends and, to my surprise, it took off! Within six months, I quit my job. To this day, I couldn't be happier that I took the chance.

Back to the present, just after surgery - as you can imagine now, I had to take a full month off for my body to heal. It wasn't easy since I get bored easily. But family and friends made the time go fast and, at the end of the month, my husband and I took a small vacation to California to visit our son.

My son, Jared, had just started his new job at Google in Mountainview, California, a few months prior. We

had a wonderful time each day! It was fun-filled and packed with activities. I planned one day to go to the Monterey Aquarium and then walk around the town. The next day we went to San Francisco to tour Alcatraz and explore Fisherman's Wharf. On the third day, we went to the Computer Museum in Mountainview and toured Google's complex and Apple's visitors' building, both in Mountainview. On the last day, we went to San Jose to the art museum and saw an IMAX movie, and toured the city. So all these new places and being with our son kept my mind off the cancer and <u>*I suggest you do anything that makes you feel good so as not to focus exclusively on the cancer.*</u>

I was on a high but I knew radiation was just around there corner when I got back to my home. When I returned from California, my mom took me to the surgeon's office to remove the tape over the stitches. Great news: found out that it was Stage 1, Grade 2 so I only needed 4 rounds of radiation that would start in November.

Chapter 7 Radiation

Only 4 Rounds But it Felt Like an Eternity

(Fourth Step Toward Better Health)

I was so nervous and had so much anxiety going to radiation, especially the first time, so my mom and BFF went with me. I was shaking and even though my doctor put me on anti-anxiety medicine, it didn't seem to calm my nerves. I couldn't eat and lost a lot of weight. I became underweight and that wasn't good at all.

It was internal radiation where they put a large bullet size and shaped metal piece into my vaginal cavity. I felt humiliated throughout this part. The first time you go they have to map out the specific area to target the radiation in the exact spot. The procedure takes 6 minutes but the whole visit takes 3 hours in and out of the CT scan machine. This was all precautionary so the cancer wouldn't spread. The CT scan showed I was clean throughout my body after my surgery. This means the cancer was all contained in the uterus so that is why the uterus, fallopian tubes, and ovaries were removed for surgery but I still had my cervix. I had to go four times and each time I brought a friend with me for moral support. Lesson learned: bring a friend or family member to doctor's visits to ease the stress.

It was worse than I thought it would be. I had terrible anxiety and my doctor upped my medicine but it really didn't help much. Mind you, I continued to do easy exercises and light yoga to help calm me down. I even tried meditation and saltwater pool therapy. Saltwater pool therapy is where you go naked into a highly salted bath. Unfortunately, my only response was to feel stung. Nothing worked, so, throughout November (I pursued my organizing business, part-time) I went once a week to the Radiation Center. Every time was an uphill battle and I felt horrible and violated. Finally, when it was over, my nerves calmed down and then my eating went back to normal. Luckily, I already had our annual vacation planned. I was excited to go to a tropical island and really relax. I thought that then I would enjoy my life once again. I did water aerobics and Yoga every day, which made me feel wonderful. *Socializing a lot was so good for my soul and, I promise, will be for you, too.*

Our vacation was wonderful and we enjoyed every minute. When I returned home, I went back to my organizing business, full-time. Year-end is a busy time of year for me since everyone wants their home ready to host family and friends for the holidays.

I knew that soon I would go to Florida and enjoy the sunshine again! It was a wonderful winter in Florida. Allan came down and visited us twice and he was also able to see his mom who lives there in the winter. I made a lot of new friends in Florida and it felt like being in a sleepaway camp. Every day was water aerobics, Yoga, aerobics, and movies and shows. We played Mah Jong once a week and every day was pool time. My BFF Pam also came down for 2 weeks and stayed 1 week with me. We went on our friend Lori's boat several times and had a great time at the craft fairs every weekend. We went out to lunch and dinner so many times. *Whatever enjoyment you can find is a big help with healing.*

Eventually, I had to go home to get back to the real world. Then, life stopped. COVID-19 shut everything down on March 15. My business was dead. No one expected guests so there was no need for my organizing services. My husband was brave enough to food shop and I was thankful that everyone was home. Google, where our son Jared worked, shut down the office so I convinced him to leave California and work from home. I was content knowing everyone was safe at home. At this time, my parents decided to stay in Florida permanently and not come home so they gave me the task of unloading their things in their New York home to charity and having the items they wanted in Florida, trucked down by a moving company. My anxiety returned with a vengeance and luckily my brother and sister-in-law and our kids helped with this huge task.

Lesson learned: Ask for help when you need it.

It was very hard for me to concentrate but I knew this was the best thing for my parents. My dad was less mobile as his Parkinson's Disease had progressed and my mom was happy there with sunshine and flowers every day. We eventually cleaned out the apartment by Face Timing with my parents almost every day. The moving company was terrific; they were very reliable and packed up all their housewares and furniture into the truck in one morning. I highly recommend Hall-Lane Van Line Movers based in Commack, NY.

Chapter 8 Oh God!

It Came Back 2 Years Later 2021

(Fifth Step Toward Better Health)

For the first two years after my hysterectomy, I had to get an internal exam every three months from my surgeon. And every six months, a CT scan. Three years after that, every 6 months, get an internal exam and a CT scan once a year.

Then something awful happened. The radiologist saw a tumor on the scan of my lung so I had a biopsy on my lung. I was nervous about the pain I would be in for a biopsy on my lung but they put me out and got the results several days later. I was devasted to find out it was cancerous in four spots on my right lung. 'What happens now?' I thought. Am I going to die? My life flashed in front of me. I was in the doctor's office at Stony Brook University Hospital, the one who performed the biopsy and he proceeded to tell me that I had Stage 4 Cancer! Uterine Cancer that metastasized into my lungs.

Oh My God! Oh My God! That's what I kept saying. I felt faint but knew since I was alone that I had to stay focused. The doctor brought in a nurse to escort me to the waiting room where I could get my breath back and then drive myself home. How was I going to tell my family? I had a hundred questions, which I planned to ask when I would meet with the oncologist. I immediately thought of my client who was an oncologist for Sloan Kettering Hospital and who specialized in women's diseases. I knew she was working so I texted her. She got back to me pretty fast and had her nurse get me in to see her the following week. In the meantime, however, she asked to have my biopsy results sent to her along with the history of the hysterectomy from 2019. Being organized definitely pays when you are in a bind.

So, the lesson to learn is always keep very good files of your medical results of any kind just in case you need to give them to another doctor and for your own piece of mind.

Chapter 9 My Oncologist

(Sixth Step Toward Better Health)

Boy, was I lucky to have as a client an oncologist who worked at Memorial Sloan Kettering Cancer Center on Long Island. I was beside myself but she assured me that she would take the best protocol for me since she specialized in women's cancer.  So, I had to send all my history to her and within days I had a consultation with her. My husband went with me to Sloan and my mom and BFF were on FaceTime on our iPhones to hear directly from her what the next steps were.

On Tuesday, July 6, I went with Allan to Memorial Sloan Kettering Cancer Center (MSKCC) where Dr. T. was an oncologist. I went with my journal in my hand with many questions. I felt great since I knew the oncologist would have my best interests at heart.

So here is the protocol she planned for me:

A. I was going to have: 2 chemotherapy treatments intravenously:

> 1- Taxol
> 2- Carboplatin

Five hours total and it would be six treatments every three weeks. The dreaded question came up rather quickly. Will I lose my hair? Yes. That's when I broke down and cried. I loved my long, beautiful blonde hair. My mom said she would come to New York and go with me to get a great wig. "We will pick a beautiful wig for you," she said. , which helped me calm down. I was still nervous but I knew I had to know the answers so I could prepare.

"Besides hair loss what other side effects would I experience?" I asked

1. Nausea- after treatment
2. Fatigue- 3 to 5 days after treatment
3. Kidney issues- must drink more water; at least two liters to keep my kidney function

4. Neuropathy- numbness in tips of fingers and toes. Use ice packs to lessen the effect

5. Mouth sores- baking soda rinse

6. Higher infection rate- take temperature when I feel warm

7. Skin sensitivity to the sun- wear rash guards

As soon as she started telling me all the side effects of chemotherapy, I almost fainted. Anxiety kicked in again. So, she prescribed Xanax in addition to my other medicines.

B. Immunotherapy - not FDA approved so I would be put on a clinical trial. The side effects were: 1. Thyroiditis and pneumonitis (inflammation) 2. Diarrhea/constipation.

Oh Boy! 'What was I getting into?' I thought. I guess this will have to happen for me to fight this cancer! So, we whipped out the calendar and set the 6 dates of my chemo and immunotherapy treatments. I felt in control because I knew those were the dates that set aside for my life-saving drugs. That's just how I thought of them.

Now, luckily, as I've written earlier, I was a swimmer and never smoked so I had that advantage. My breathing and lungs were great and working exceptionally well. You would never know I had cancer again but, of course, the anxiety came back. This was the worst, so I found another therapist who put me on different anxiety medicine (I went on Prozac) and she increased it twice and put me on sleep medicine (I went on Olanzapine). I finally got my body to stop having anxiety attacks.

With the list of side effects I anticipated, this is what I did to get ready for this chapter in my life:

1. Hair falls out everywhere on your body- not just your head, so when my mom flew up from Florida,  we went to a reputable wig store to get fitted and order a real hair wig that was highlighted and the same exact color and a little longer than my current hair. Bought several turbans and a baseball cap with a ponytail attached in the back that I would wear while on organizing jobs.

2. Nausea- filied a prescription for anti-nausea medication (which fortunately never had to take).

3. Fatigue- the 3-5 days after treatment was what I feared most since I had a physical job. I decided to rest and didn't plan any jobs the day after my treatments.

4. Strain on your kidneys- drank a lot of water, more than normal two liters/day. This was easy since it was still summer.

5. Neuropathy – iced my feet and hands during treatment

6. Mouth sores- I rinsed a lot with mouthwash

7. Higher infection rate- COVID made it more complicated. So, I was double-masked when in public, and on the plane I wore a shield. Also, I never worked or socialized with anyone who wasn't vaccinated.

8. Sensitivity to the sun- kept my body covered in the summer sun, which was challenging. I bought rash guards online and always wore a hat.

I felt I was in great hands with Dr. T. who was an oncologist with wonderful credentials and had been practicing in this cancer area of expertise for 30 years. She also recommended that I go into a clinical trial for immunology, which had been showing amazing results. It would cause my treatment to start two weeks later than planned (originally scheduled for July 30th) but she highly recommended it; I asked her: if her daughter was in this situation would she wait and she said "absolutely!" So, I took her advice, trusted her, and waited until August 10th.

What I learned: *ask the questions that will keep you informed, rarely surprised, and able to prepare. Most importantly: select doctors you trust!*

Chapter 10 The Day at Memorial Sloan Kettering Cancer Center (MSKCC)

(Seventh Step Toward Better Health)

August 10: It was my first day of chemo and taking Xanax that morning for the first time seemed to do the trick. The anxiety was under control and my first (out of 6) chemo and immunology therapies went smoothly. I was very impressed with how organized the whole process was.

It's a whole day event. I pack a duffle bag with my phone charger, my iPad and charger, a soft wrap, and my lunch with several drinks and snacks. You get there in the morning, you wait a while before you see the intake nurse who takes your vitals (temperature, blood pressure, oxygen levels). I then got weighed and the nurse takes two vials of blood that immediately go to the lab in-house. This makes sure my white blood cell count is in the normal range so my body could accept the chemotherapy. Then I'd wait to speak to the research nurse because I was on a clinical trial for immunology (Keytruda through IV also). She asked a long list of questions, especially about any side effects I had and also general health questions. She reviewed my meds and nutritional supplements. All done on the computer.

Afterward, I waited awhile in the room while my oncologist reviewed the blood results taken about two hours prior. Then she comes into the exam room. Luckily, it's a private room with a USB port to charge my phone. Talking and texting friends wanting to know what's happening. Dr. T. comes in and said we are good to go but first, she listens to my lungs with her stethoscope. She asks me many questions and then I ask her questions and then I go back to the waiting room to be called for a treatment room.

This wait time could take up to two hours depending on how busy they are. They have 26 treatment rooms. I prefer the window rooms, so I can see the weather and other activity; remember - I am there all day.

Once I am settled, my husband leaves and goes to his work office. I already scheduled a friend to visit every 2 hours: 12-2 pm, 2-4 pm, 4-6 pm, and 6-8 pm. My friends Pam and Larissa came after Allan left to go to work. So, I was never alone. I planned every treatment to have a friend come every two hours. I was there usually the entire day so many of them obliged me and enjoyed the time we spent talking while I was receiving my therapy. The nurses thought we were having a party since every time I came, I wore pink, the color that always made me happy.

At this time, I was only allowed one guest in the room due to COVID. A form must be filled out by–me and the guest 1-2 days before treatment over the MSKCC portal. Very organized! My friends text me when they have arrived in the waiting room so I send out the visitor who's currently with me. I am never alone. It makes the day go by so fast. I also FaceTime others who are at work or are out of town during my therapy.

There is a pre-intravenous (IV) regimen before I start the chemo. First, anti-nausea then Benadryl IV, and then steroid IV. Once those are all done they put me on Taxol for three hours while I have to put my feet and hands on ice to avoid neuropathy. It worked. It's uncomfortable but they usually feel hot so it's not so bad. My friends distract me. I eat lunch with them and again FaceTime with other friends. The nurses are very friendly and professional so it makes the time as enjoyable as can be.

Then 30 minutes of Carboplaton therapy (Carbo), which is the second cocktail with my chemotherapy. After Carbo is completed, I then get immunotherapy. Then when I know when I will be finished with my two chemo cocktails and immunotherapy, I text my husband to pick me up, since we started at different times through all six sessions. It makes it less stressful for him and he can get more work done in the office instead of waiting around as he did all morning.

After my third treatment, I had to go for another CT scan. That was great news: the tumors shrank tremendously and I was on the road to remission! I then had to plan something fun to do. Being an organizer, I love doing this kind of stuff! And, of course, it would shift my focus from cancer to pleasure.

So, I planned another short trip. Allan and I went to see our son, Jared, in Austin, Texas. Jared had left Google and since taken a dream job with a company that makes mobile video games. I had never been to Texas. The planning was very exciting and I needed a change of pace. When we arrived Jared was still working so we went to a restaurant I had seen on Facebook that was all pink. I mean the tables, the chairs, the plates and glasses, all the beautiful décor was pink. Remember – it's my happy color! This was a simple yet very fun thing to plan; you can do it, too!

For my birthday weekend, we visited with Jared and saw Austin and San Antonio. After we ate at the pink restaurant, we went to our hotel to check in and then picked up Jared to go on a Haunted Ghost Story Walking Tour. It was very interesting and I never knew Austin was known for their bats. Afterward, we went to a historical landmark that was converted into an authentic Texan restaurant. It was so old and we could see the age of the floor and the original walls from the 1800s!

The next day, which was my actual birthday, we planned a day in San Antonio to see the Alamo and River Walk. I was so impressed with the history and culture of the place. The weather was also perfect to walk around this happening town. Jared bought me a pink cowgirl hat with a tiara, which I wore all day so as not to be reminded of my bald head and then I

found a pair of brown boots with the pink ribbon (breast cancer) logo stitch all over it. They were on sale so it was an exciting find! Besides getting the guided tour of the Alamo we also took a boat ride through the River Walk, which I absolutely loved.

We got to see the entire area from the water side. There were so many restaurants, music venues, and stores. The only thing that disappointed me was that it was so noisy, I couldn't hear the person giving the guided tour. So, after we got off, I went to the courtesy desk and explained my situation: it was my birthday and I was really looking forward to the boat tour however, I couldn't hear the guided docent. And they were so nice about it and gave us three free tickets to go on the boat tour again; we decided to go after dinner so we could experience it in the evening.

We then walked to the tallest building in San Antonio, the Tower of America, which was built for San Antonio's World's Fair in 1968. The views were spectacular. I discovered that because I received so many texts and Facebook messages and e-mails my cell phone had died. So, I used Allan's the rest of the day. Then we went back to the river walk to listen to the Mariachi band in the amphitheater that was performing and then we had dinner. We decided to eat an authentic Mexican dinner. The food was delicious and not too spicy.

Afterward, we took the boat ride however this time it was so dazzling with all the colored lights everywhere, and we easily heard the docent this time so I really enjoyed the boat ride experience.

Lesson learned: *never be afraid to ask for what you want!*

The next day was Halloween and we had a wonderful brunch at a rooftop restaurant called Paper Boy. Jared had been there with his girlfriend before and really enjoyed the food so we went and I had Mexican-style breakfast burritos. They were very tasty. Afterward, we went to South Congress Area (very much like Brooklyn, NY) where there was also a craft fair so I treated myself to some jewelry. We then went back to Jared's apartment to get the key so we could see his workspace.

I was very impressed with the place. It was decorated so casually and had plenty of space to play video games, arcade games, foosball, and air hockey. They had three refrigerators stocked with drinks and snacks for the employees. After seeing where Jared worked, we took some pictures and then said goodbye since we had to get to the airport with time to first return the rental car. It was great seeing Jared and I understood why he liked it there. We had a layover in Nashville, another first, but we only ate dinner there and then flew home to New York.

The next day, after we returned, I did my wash and then went to the mall with my friend, Ellen to use all my birthday gift certificates I had received and then had lunch with her. I told her all about my exciting trip and the next day, of course, I scrapbooked the trip while it was fresh in my memory. After going to the drug store to develop all the pictures, I scrapbooked the trip with brochures and other items. I finished the book so now I could show all my friends and family.

Lesson learned: *there are so many ways to extend a good time, whether by reminiscing with friends or creating mementos with a scrapbook and photos!*

My last chemo was on November 30th, a day I will never forget! I got there at 8:30 am and wanted to get the day done so we could celebrate afterward. So, by 10 am I had my first visitor, Randee, then Hillary then Sue. Every two hours I was allowed to have a visitor. The last one for my chemo treatment was my BFF, Pam and then Hillary returned at the very end so she

could see me ring the bell to signify that I completed my chemotherapy. Boy, what a thrill that was! Hillary videotaped it and Pam took pics.

Afterward, with my two friends, my brother, and his family, we all went to a Mexican restaurant, which had a very lively atmosphere and did we have fun! I was so happy that I couldn't remember the last time I was this happy.

Two weeks later, I was taking my annual vacation to Aruba and I was on a high. As usual, I would be going with family and friends and it would be a time to relax and celebrate. I would be in Aruba for a week before returning to Long Island, for the last lap of my cancer journey. This was called immunotherapy (Keytruda through IV but it's only 30 minutes, not the entire day). For the next two years, I will receive it every six weeks to keep cancer from coming back. They call it maintenance.

Lesson learned: *never miss an opportunity to celebrate what you can!*

Chapter 11 Maintenance Program

(Eighth Step Toward Better Health)

Before I started the maintenance program, I had to plan my daughter's move to Brooklyn, New York. She had found a very nice apartment that had two bedrooms, renovated kitchen, and a bathroom. It was finally time for her to take the plunge. Even though she was still working remotely for Goldman Sachs, she felt it was time for her to live on her own.

We were excited for her and wanted to make it as easy as possible, so on the day of her move, December 4th we rented a U-Haul truck to pack up all of the things she wanted from our home and then stopped at a friend's home to pick up some furniture she had promised for Rachel that her daughter no longer used. This furniture would be used in the second bedroom for her office/studio. The rest of her furniture was being delivered by Raymore and Flanagan that day. Rachel and I picked it out a few weeks ago when she told us she was moving out.

She slept at a friend's house in Brooklyn the night before so she could get to her new apartment by 8 am when the furniture was being delivered. When we finally got there, Sam, her partner, and her friend Jake helped us unload the truck, which took 2 hours. There also was a guy off the street who offered to help, especially with the heavier items. Rachel was on the second floor but the elevator was so small we decided to just carry everything up the wide staircase. Then while Allan returned the truck, I proceed to do my thing - unpack and organize Rachel's apartment with her assisting me. I was thrilled to do this for my daughter; it was similar to getting her dorm room ready but on a larger scale. Within 4 hours everything was unpacked and placed in its rightful home.

Even the pictures were hung and the temporary paper shades were put up. The place looked wonderful and just when Allan came back, with the car now, we had dinner on the kitchen set. We ordered pizza, which is very good in Brooklyn, NY. They say it's all about the water.

December 7, I had a CT scan at MSKCC and also got a Neubrogen shot to build up my immunity since we were going on vacation soon. The following day I had to get a PCR test (Polymerase Chain Reaction), a test to detect genetic material from a specific organism such as COVID to show that I was negative to get into a foreign country. Afterward, I went to the nail salon to get my pedicure and nail tips done for Aruba. That night I had my Professional Organizers of Long Island POLI) holiday party. It was held at the Marco Polo restaurant in Westbury. We had it there last year and everyone enjoyed the private room and food. It was very nice to see my colleagues and they all complimented me on how well I looked. I wore my wig that I had styled myself so I felt really good. Dr. T. had texted me that day that my scan looks great. So, we all made a toast to my good health that night.

On December 9th, Dr. T's nurse called me to inform me that the Cancer was gone in the left lobe and the right lobe tumors were very small, almost gone. They had shrunk from centimeters to millimeters.

I WAS SO HAPPY I had to call Allan and my parents and brothers and then texted all my friends the wonderful news.

Now I could go on vacation with a clear head.

As if this day couldn't get any better, my son called to tell me he got the job he'd wanted at Facebook and he would be moving back home since it was remote. I was over the moon! Again, I had to give all this wonderful news to my family and friends before leaving for Aruba in two days.

Dec 11: Off to Aruba for a week's vacation! It was such a wonderful trip for me mentally since I didn't have to worry about my cancer. I socialized with all my friends that we had become accustomed to seeing there. The weather was great as usual and we had wonderful dinners out every night. Just one big party! Everyone couldn't get over my energy and positive outlook. I was done with chemo and I was so happy! I was surrounded by family and friends the entire week, which gave me the energy to move forward and stay inspired!

Chapter 12 Cancer in Remission

(This Book's Lessons into the World)

Throughout this journey of so many emotions, I have learned that:

- You are never alone
- You are strong and capable to get through the worst of times
- Hair will grow back and life can be as it was before cancer

I go to Memorial Sloan Kettering Cancer Center every three weeks to have my immunotherapy. It doesn't take all day so I can even work before I go for treatment. It's the standard procedure to see the intake nurse for vitals and then the research nurse since I am on a clinical trial for Keytruda. I then see my oncologist before treatment. I bring a friend with

me too so the day goes by quickly and I am not alone. We usually go to lunch first, adding a social element and, also, so that I am not hungry during the Keytruda treatment.

I continue to go for treatment every three weeks even if I have to fly home from Florida since I spend the winters there now with my parents. I am lucky

enough to still have them and they bring joy to my life! So, on January 6, 2022, I flew down to stay at my place in Delray Beach until April 21 and came back several times for treatment.

While in Florida, I stay very active. I always wanted to learn to play pickleball so, every Monday, Tuesday, and Thursday from 4-6 pm I play with others on the courts in my community. I was lucky enough to find someone who took pity on me and gave me several private lessons. I loved it and got better and better over time. It was a huge confidence booster and everyone was so nice and understanding.

Chapter 13 Conclusion

Tuesday, March 22 when I came home to Florida for my second Keytruda treatment the doctor told me I was CANCER-FREE! The nodules there are dormant and they are not spreading. YIPPIE with a big Y!

I was again so relieved to hear this news and that is when I decided to plan a 60th birthday pool party in the summer. I had a huge reason to celebrate and I love parties. Can you tell? I already had a Paris-themed party at 50 after returning from a 10-day trip to Paris with Allan and friends and again, when I turned 55, double nickels, I had a Luau party with real Hawaiian dancers performing after a catered lunch outside.

Again, I went into organizing mode. Got on my computer and typed up my guest list and then used my label maker to type 60th Birthday Party to put all my ideas and contracts in my Projects hanging folder. I do this whenever I plan anything; I make a folder so all the contents related to the event are

safely stored in one place in my office desk. So, then I took out my previous party files to get in touch with a caterer, DJ, and photographer. Table and chair rental and balloon decorator. The day I got back from Florida I took care of all the details. Sent out an e-mail to all my friends and family I was inviting. I designed the e-vite with my talented daughter Rachel.

Sunday, May 1 I tested positive for COVID after my son, Jared, tested positive for Covid who was in Florida with his girlfriend. I felt fine but Allan had a cold and he tested positive too. So, Jared quarantined in a hotel in Florida while Allan & I stayed home for a week. I don't know how I contracted it but, thank God, it was very minor; I was able to talk with clients to reschedule them and

Allan was able to do his job remotely, from home. While he was easily able to work from home, I had to plan things to do in order not to get bored, so this was a great time to write this book.

So many of my clients have urged me over the years to write a book but I never wanted to write one that many other organizers wrote about: "how to organize" and their experiences with their clients. My type of book had never been written. So here it is now! Most of this material for the book came from my two journals where I chronicled daily life since my first cancer diagnosis. This process has helped me appreciate how far I've come through this Journey.

Lesson Learned: <u>Get yourself a journal and write down your thoughts and feelings daily. Keep it by your bedside so that you remember to record in it every day.</u>

Saturday, July 16
I was excited that the day was a beautiful one weather-wise for my 60th birthday pool party. There was so much joy and cause for celebration that I was cancer free. I made a small speech thanking

everyone for all their support since day one. I wanted friends and family to know that I couldn't have gotten through any of this without their emails, texts, and phone calls.

I hope when reading this book that you will understand the emotional, physical, and mental blocks you can develop while going through cancer and how to overcome them. It is not easy but if I can do it anyone can. You just have to be determined, have perseverance, and be organized!

What I learned from having cancer twice is, first and foremost, that it is imperative to have a great support system. This way you feel you are never alone. You are strong and capable to get through the worst of times and this was the worst. Now I truly understand the marriage vows 'for better or for worse.' Health is #1 and without your health, you don't have a good life. Keep on top of your health and see a doctor when anything is not right. Continue to eat healthily and exercise. My hair will grow back and my life will be as it was before cancer. It can be for you, too. Use your personal strength and strong positive attitude to get you through the hard times.

I continue to enjoy life – concerts, shows, exhibits, craft fairs, etc. with friends and family members so you can, too! Celebrate friendships, spend time with family, explore new hobbies, and travel when possible, even if it's a day trip.

There's no promise at any time of medical results. My promise is about attitude and mindset that have been, and continue to be, the support of my medical battle and can speed and improve quality of life. My promise is about harnessing what you know, knowing how my passion for organizing has been so impactful, helping others to see beyond clutter or mess, and now applying it to my cancer disease. I hope when reading this book that you will understand the emotional, physical, and mental blocks while going through cancer and how to overcome them.

My mother and me

Whether you are dealing with cancer or any other health or personal challenge, you have to ask yourself:

Are you satisfied with your current situation?

Would you like to make some changes?

Use my thought process to clarify your goals and intentions:

1. Evaluate your life.
2. Decide what you want to continue.
3. Identify what you want to change.
4. Pinpoint the lifestyle you desire.

Your life is made up of different parts: career, personal, family, health, money, reputation, relationship with a partner, and travel. Use the organized process to assess the parts of your life you want to improve.

About the Author

Cynthia Braun realized her passion for all things organized at a very early age. Even as a young child, Cynthia constantly re-arranged her parent's house, best friend and cousin's bedrooms when visiting often, to their delight.

This is when Cynthia's parents realized that college spent at the Alpha Kappa Phi Sorority's impeccably organized home made an indelible mark on Cynthia as House President. Cynthia has since spent the next 25 years helping her friends, relatives, and co-workers declutter and simplify their lives.

Throughout the years, Cynthia has honed her skills as an organizing wizard in everything she does. From Cynthia's former career in sales & marketing with such companies as Goodyear Tire and Rubber Company and Lepel Corporation, to the extensive volunteer work for which she has a passion; Cynthia always finds ways of making everything she touches run more smoothly.

After a successful Sales & Marketing career, Cynthia decided to follow her true calling and started "Organize Your Life" in 2002. Since then, Cynthia has been busy helping individuals, families, and businesses with their many organizational needs. Cynthia is a Golden Circle member of the National Association of Productivity and Organizing Professionals (NAPO) and was on their national board from 2006-9. She is the founding member of POLI, Professional Organizers of Long Island. In 2013 she realized that, by adding Feng Shui to her skill set, she would be able to help her clients even more. She attended Metropolitan Institute of Design to get certified in Feng Shui. Now Cynthia is a Red Ribbon Consultant with the International Feng Shui Guild. The highest level one can achieve.

Cynthia has been active in her local community, supporting a variety of civic endeavors. Since 1992, she has been an active volunteer and board member of Hadassah, serving as President, Fundraiser VP, Membership VP and Programming VP. For 7 years she was a mentor in NAPO's mentoring program, assisting new professional organizers with their business plan & objectives. From 1997– 2011 she served an active role in Stony Brook's Temple Isaiah Sisterhood as Membership VP and was responsible for a variety of creative & successful fund-raising events, especially the most attended event, the Annual Fashion Show which she coordinated.

She has been profiled, interviewed and published in many newspapers and online magazines and blogs, including Newsday, NY Magazine, Closet Magazine. And she's frequently a resource for Long Island Newsday business reporters and organizing books. She has appeared on several radio stations as the Organizing Expert.

A strong believer that small business ownership is a powerful way to build and enjoy a good life, she's a frequent speaker for Long Island networking and trade groups as well as an interview subject. She's published 3 E-books, *Organizing Your Garage, Organizing Your Kitchen, Organizing Your Home Office.* In 2013, she again started the Long Island group for Feng Shui practitioners on Long Island. Cynthia grew up on Long Island and obtained an M.B.A. in Marketing at Adelphi University in Garden City. She also attended the Metropolitan School of Interior Design in Plainview. She fills her free time with scrapbooking (her other passion for 35 years) traveling with family and friends while enjoying all that Long Island, New York City, and southern Florida offers.

You can find her at her website:
www.OrganizeYourLife.org
You can connect with her by e-mail:
ckbraun@optonline.net

NOTES

NOTES